FAMOUS FIGURES
OF THE
RENAISSANCE

MOVABLE PAPER FIGURES TO CUT, COLOR, AND ASSEMBLE

CATHY DIEZ-LUCKIE

FIGURES IN MOTION®

LIVERMORE, CALIFORNIA

Published by
Figures In Motion
2150 Cabernet Way
Livermore, CA 94550
(925) 583-5670
E-mail: info@FiguresInMotion.com
Web: http://www.FiguresInMotion.com

© 2015 Figures In Motion
ISBN 978-0-9818566-6-7

Quantity Discounts Available
Books published by Figures In Motion are available for bulk purchase at special quantity discount to individuals, businesses, schools, museums, associations, and other institutions.
For discount schedule and terms, contact us at info@FiguresInMotion.com or call us at (925) 583-5670.

Manufactured by Regent Publishing Services, Hong Kong
Printed March 2015 in ShenZhen, Guangdong, China
10 9 8 7 6 5 4 3 2 1

This book is dedicated to my husband, Brian Goodman, with gratitude for all the encouragement and help he has given me through the completion of this project. Thank you to Mary Jo Tate for editing the text of this book.

How to Use This Book

For Children...

- Now you can make real moving figures of ten of the most important people from the Renaissance. Color your own costumes or use figures that have already been colored. Cut them out, put them together with fasteners, and make them move. Act out the real stories of history or make up your own and travel through time with moving figures!

- You can make puppets by attaching craft sticks or pipe cleaners to the moving figures or make stop-motion animation clips with magnets or felt attached to the back of the figures. Download our scripts or create your own to act out the history of the Renaissance.

For Parents and Educators...

- *Famous Figures of the Renaissance* provides hands-on activities for children to study some of the people who shaped our world. Children love to use crayons, colored pencils, scissors, and paper to create things. This book gives you a creative way to teach history by using activities that naturally appeal to them. Children will color, cut out, and assemble figures that really move! Each figure has been printed on sturdy paper and may be assembled with mini brads. Hole punches and fasteners are available at most craft stores or on our website.

- All of the illustrations in this book are true to period costume. In addition to the line drawings, we've provided color figures for children who would rather focus on the assembly and use of the figures. The back of each figure is labeled by name for easy identification after assembly.

- The *Famous Figures* series reinforces your children's history lessons and encourages them to study the great men and women of the past. Galileo, Elizabeth I, and William Shakespeare will come alive as children create their real moving figures. The book may be used independently or combined with any history curriculum that covers the Renaissance.

- Internet-linked scripts, coloring pages, puzzles, and activities are available at FiguresInMotion.com.

For Museums and Historical Reenactors...

- Inform and educate children about leaders from the Renaissance as they visit your museum's collection or special exhibition. Let children take home a remembrance of what they experienced at your museum with *Famous Figures of the Renaissance*.

- The *Famous Figures* series is useful in generating interest for historical reenactments. Costumes are meticulously drawn and historically accurate.

CONTENTS

Luminaries of the Renaissance

Johannes Gutenberg—a German goldsmith, blacksmith, publisher, and printer—was one of the most influential people in history with his innovation of movable type printing. His invention launched the printing revolution that led to the mass production of printed books and changed society forever. Gutenberg's greatest work, the Gutenberg Bible (also known as the 42-line Bible) was first printed in 1455. Most of the approximately 180 copies were printed on paper, but some were on vellum. The first printed Bible was arranged in two columns and lacked paragraphs, indentation, and page numbers.

Gutenberg's process for the mass production of movable type, the use of oil-based ink, and the use of a wooden printing press spread quickly throughout Europe and eventually the world. Pamphlets and books became readily available and were used to spread new ideas, threatening the political and religious establishments and bringing about radical changes in education and trade.

Christopher Columbus—an Italian navigator, admiral, and explorer—completed four voyages across the Atlantic Ocean, increasing European appreciation of America and claiming land for the Spanish crown. He launched a new era of European exploration, conquest, and colonization that lasted several hundred years.

As navigators competed to find a sea route to Asia to obtain silk and spices from China after the fall of Constantinople, Columbus convinced the Spanish monarchs, Ferdinand II and Isabella I, to support him in his quest to reach the East Indies by sailing westward. He left Spain in 1492 with an expedition of three ships, stopped in the Canary Islands to restock, and landed in San Salvador. During his travels, Columbus discovered the trade winds but never reached his goal. Though he was not the first explorer to reach the Americas, he established settlements on the island of Hispaniola that began the Spanish colonization of the New World.

Isabella I, queen of Castile and León, reigned with her husband, Ferdinand II, in Spain. She was named as heir to the throne of her older half-brother, Henry IV, and was secretly betrothed to Ferdinand II of Aragon. She understood the importance of having a strong financial position and eliminated the enormous debt that her brother, Henry IV, had left after his reign.

While Isabella and Ferdinand are most known for sponsoring Christopher Columbus's voyage of 1492 that led to the discovery of the New World, they also brought stability to the Spanish kingdoms that eventually led to the unification of Spain under their grandson, the Holy Roman Emperor Charles V. They ordered that all Muslim and Jewish subjects convert to Christianity or be exiled. Isabella and Ferdinand transformed the administration of Spain and used a police force to establish law and order, greatly reducing the crime rate to the lowest it had been in years.

Leonardo da Vinci, one of the greatest painters in history, was an Italian sculptor, architect, engineer, inventor, anatomist, musician, geologist, cartographer, botanist, writer, and perhaps the most accomplished man of the Renaissance. His gift of painting was seen during his apprenticeship in the workshop of Verrocchio, where his work excelled over the others. He became a highly sought-after artist with commissions all over Europe. His paintings included *Annunciation*, *The Last Supper*, and the *Mona Lisa*. His most famous drawing was the *Vitruvian Man*, a study of the proportions of the human body.

Leonardo kept many notebooks filled with artistic studies, small sketches, and drawings of things that interested him, with most of his writing done in mirror-image cursive. He was not trained as a scientist, but he observed and recorded the world around him, was valued as an engineer, and was fascinated with flight and the creation of various machines.

Michelangelo—an Italian sculptor, painter, architect, and engineer—was one of the greatest artists of his time. Sponsored by sovereigns and popes, his paintings, sculpture, and works of architecture have been celebrated throughout history. The vast number of Michelangelo's works and his surviving sketches, correspondence, and writings make him one of the most documented artists of the sixteenth century. He was the first Western artist to have his biography published while he was alive.

Michelangelo's scenes from Genesis, painted on the ceiling of the Sistine Chapel in Rome, contain over three hundred figures. Along with *The Last Judgment*, painted on the altar wall of the same chapel, they are renowned in the history of Western art. As architect of St. Peter's Basilica, he transformed the western end of the basilica, but the dome was completed after his death. His sculptures of the Pietà and David, acclaimed for their beauty, established Michelangelo as a master sculptor.

Martin Luther, a Catholic priest excommunicated from the church and condemned as an outlaw, was a German monk, professor of theology, founder of the Lutheran Church, and a key figure of the Protestant Reformation. He taught that salvation was a free gift of God's grace through faith alone in Christ and could not be earned by good deeds; this became the foundation for the Reformation. He translated the Bible from Latin into German and taught that it was the only source of man's knowledge about God.

As the church came to Germany, selling indulgences to raise money to rebuild St. Peter's Basilica, Luther questioned his bishop in a letter about this practice, pointing out that man could not purchase freedom from God's punishment for sin. That letter, which became known as the Ninety-Five Theses, was translated into German, was widely circulated throughout Europe, and ultimately threatened the authority of the church.

Henry VIII, king of England, was known for his six marriages and his role in the separation of the Church of England from the pope and the Roman Catholic Church. He was the second monarch of the Tudor dynasty, assumed the kingship of Ireland, and was one of the founders of the Royal Navy.

Henry's first two queens—Catherine of Aragon and Anne Boleyn, mother of the future Elizabeth I—failed to give him a male heir. Motivated by his desperate desire for a male successor, Henry went through a series of divorces and remarriages that was strongly criticized by the pope, whom Henry saw as a stumbling block to accomplishing his goals. Since the church would not cooperate and annul his successive marriages, Henry left the church and initiated the English Reformation, changing the country to a Protestant one and establishing royal supremacy over the church.

Elizabeth I, daughter of Henry VIII and Anne Boleyn, succeeded her older half-sister Mary (daughter of Catherine of Aragon) to the throne. The last monarch of the Tudor dynasty, Elizabeth was intelligent and determined, and she surrounded herself with astute ministers to help rule the country. Elizabeth established the English Protestant church, which later became the Church of England. She oversaw one of the greatest military victories in English history, defeating the Spanish Armada (a fleet of 130 ships) as Philip II of Spain attempted to conquer England in 1588 to overthrow her reign and defeat Protestantism.

The Elizabethan era was characterized by a thriving English theater, with playwrights such as William Shakespeare and Christopher Marlowe, and by the conquests of English explorers Sir Francis Drake and Sir Walter Raleigh. Elizabeth was often called Good Queen Bess and Gloriana because the image of her reign was one of triumph.

LUMINARIES OF THE RENAISSANCE

William Shakespeare is considered one of the greatest playwrights and poets of all time. The son of John Shakespeare, a successful leather merchant who served as alderman, he was baptized in the English town of Stratford-upon-Avon in 1564 and is believed to have attended King Edward VI School.

Starting his career in the theater as an actor and a playwright, Shakespeare became a managing partner in a popular acting company in London, the Lord Chamberlain's Men, which changed to the King's Men after the coronation of King James I. By the end of the century, Shakespeare had completed fifteen of his thirty-seven known plays and built the Globe Theatre in London with his business partners. Shakespeare was able to continue to write almost full time due to his successful investments. His early works consisted mainly of histories and comedies, followed by tragedies that included *Hamlet*, *King Lear*, *Othello*, and *Macbeth*.

Galileo Galilei—an Italian astronomer, mathematician, physicist, and engineer—was a key contributor to the advancement of observational astronomy and physics during the scientific revolution. After hearing about Dutch telescopes, Galileo designed more powerful versions. With them he confirmed the phases of Venus, viewed the surface of the moon, discovered the four largest moons of Jupiter, and observed sunspots. He referred to himself as "the first observer of marvelous things." He also described the first accurate laws of motion for masses.

Galileo defended and made observations supporting heliocentrism, a model in which Earth and the other planets revolve around the Sun, first presented by

Nicolaus Copernicus and enhanced by Johannes Kepler. This model was in opposition to geocentrism, which placed Earth at the orbital center of all the heavenly bodies. Isaac Newton expanded upon Galileo's work and demonstrated that gravitational force was responsible for the orbits of the planets in the solar system.

Famous Figures of the Renaissance Reading List
Read–Alouds and Books for Independent Readers

Fine Print: A Story about Johann Gutenberg by Joann Johansen Burch
Who in the World Was the Secretive Printer?
    The Story of Johannes Gutenberg by Robert Beckham

Christopher Columbus by Stephen Krensky
First Voyage to America: From the Log of the "Santa Maria" by
    Christopher Columbus
Meet Christopher Columbus by James T. de Kay
The World of Columbus and Sons by Genevieve Foster
Who Was Christopher Columbus? by Bonnie Bader

Da Vinci by Mike Venezia
Leonardo da Vinci by Diane Stanley
Leonardo da Vinci (Landmark) by Emily Hahn
*Leonardo da Vinci: Artist, Inventor and Scientist of the
    Renaissance* by Francesca Romei
Leonardo da Vinci for Kids: His Life and Ideas by Janis Herbert
Leonardo da Vinci: The Genius Who Defined the Renaissance by
    John Phillips
Who Was Leonardo da Vinci? by Roberta Edwards

Michelangelo by Diane Stanley
Michelangelo by Mike Venezia
Michelangelo: Master of the Italian Renaissance by Gabriella Di Cagno
Stone Giant: Michelangelo's David and How He Came to Be by
    Jane Sutcliffe

Luther the Leader by Virgil E. Robinson
Martin Luther: A Man Who Changed the World by Paul Maier

Good Queen Bess: The Story of Elizabeth I of England by Diane
    Stanley and Peter Vennema
Elizabeth I: The Outcast Who Became England's Queen by Simon Adams
Queen Elizabeth and the Spanish Armada (Landmark) by Frances Winwar
Who Was Queen Elizabeth? by June Eding

Bard of Avon: The Story of William Shakespeare by Diane Stanley and
    Peter Vennema
Shakespeare for Kids: His Life and Times by Colleen Aagesen
Who Was William Shakespeare? by Celeste Mannis
Will Shakespeare and the Globe Theater (Landmark) by Anne Terry White
William Shakespeare and the Globe by Aliki

Galileo for Kids: His Life and Ideas by Richard Panchyk
Galileo: The Genius Who Charted the Universe by Philip Steele
I, Galileo by Bonnie Christensen
Starry Messenger: Galileo Galilei by Peter Sis

Additional Reading: The Renaissance
Mary, Queen of Scots (Landmark) by Emily Hahn
Ferdinand Magellan: Master Mariner (Landmark) by Seymour Gates Pond
Walter Raleigh: Man of Two Worlds (Landmark) by Henrietta Buckmaster

H
Front

F
Front

H
Back

A
Front

F
Back

C
Back

G
Front

A
Back

B
Back

Johannes Gutenberg
Inventor of Movable Type Printing

E
Front

D
Back

E
Back

B
Front

© Figures In Motion
www.figuresinmotion.com

G
Back

C
Front

D
Front

H
Front

F
Front

H
Back

A
Front

F
Back

C
Back

G
Front

A
Back

B
Back

Johannes Gutenberg
Inventor of Movable Type Printing

E
Front

D
Back

E
Back

B
Front

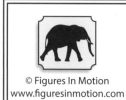

© Figures In Motion
www.figuresinmotion.com

G
Back

C
Front

D
Front

B
Back

D
Back

H
Back

F
Back

H
Front

A
Back

B
Front

E
Back

F
Front

C
Back

C
Front

Christopher Columbus
Navigator, Admiral, and Explorer

G
Back

A
Front

G
Front

D
Front

E
Front

B
Back

D
Back

H
Back

F
Back

H
Front

A
Back

ɘɒᙠ
E

ʇnoɿꟻ
F

B
Front

C
Back

Christopher Columbus
Navigator, Admiral, and Explorer

C
Front

© Figures In Motion
www.figuresinmotion.com

ᙠɒɔk
G

ʇnoɿꟻ
A

ʇnoɿꟻ
G

D
Front

E
Front

The scepter may be used without fasteners and attached to Isabella's hands with tape. Position as desired.

E
Front

A
Back

B
Front

D
Front

C
Back

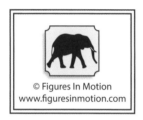

Isabella I
Queen of Castile and León

C
Front

A
Front

D
Back

B
Back

E
Back

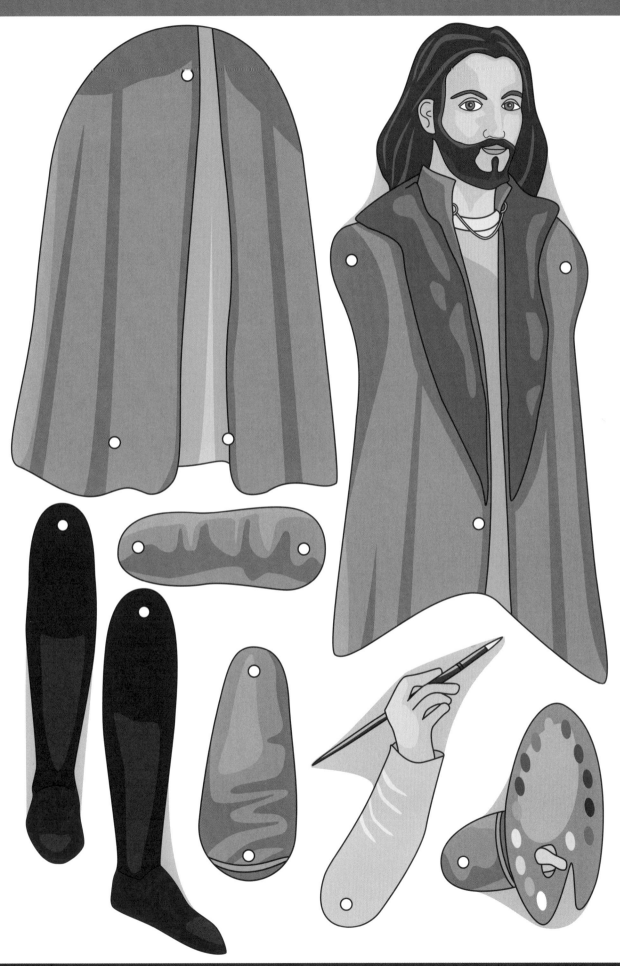

A
Front

B
Back

Leonardo da Vinci
Painter, Sculptor, Architect, Musician, Cartographer, Engineer, Inventor, Writer, and Botanist

© Figures In Motion
www.figuresinmotion.com

C
Front

E
Front

D
Front

G
Back

A
Back

D
Back

E
Back

B
Front

Front

F

G
Front

F
Back

A
Front

B
Back

Leonardo da Vinci
Painter, Sculptor, Architect, Musician, Cartographer, Engineer, Inventor, Writer, and Botanist

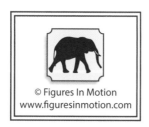

E
Front

D
Front

C
Front

G
Back

A
Back

D
Back

E
Back

B
Front

Front

F

G
Front

F
Back

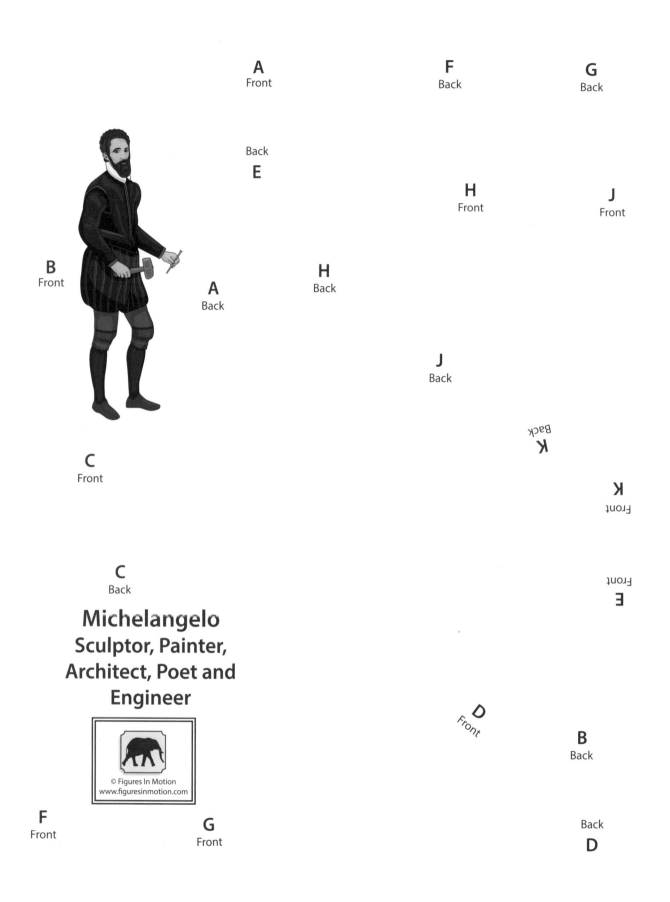

A
Front

F
Back

G
Back

Back
E

H
Front

J
Front

B
Front

A
Back

H
Back

J
Back

C
Front

K
Back

K
Front

C
Back

E
Front

Michelangelo
Sculptor, Painter,
Architect, Poet and
Engineer

D
Front

B
Back

© Figures In Motion
www.figuresinmotion.com

F
Front

G
Front

Back
D

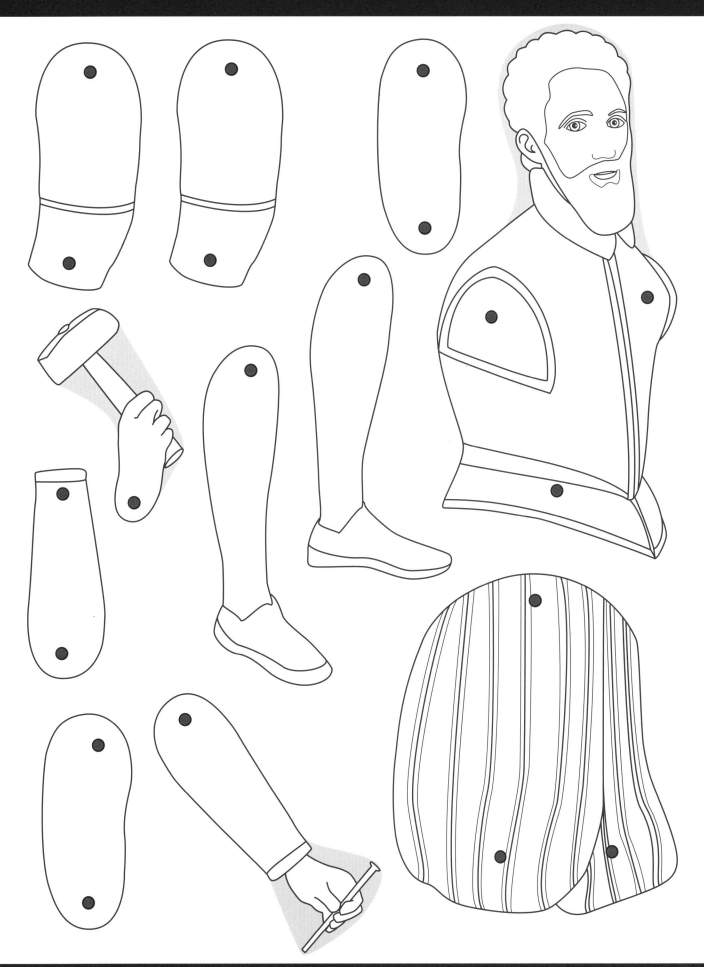

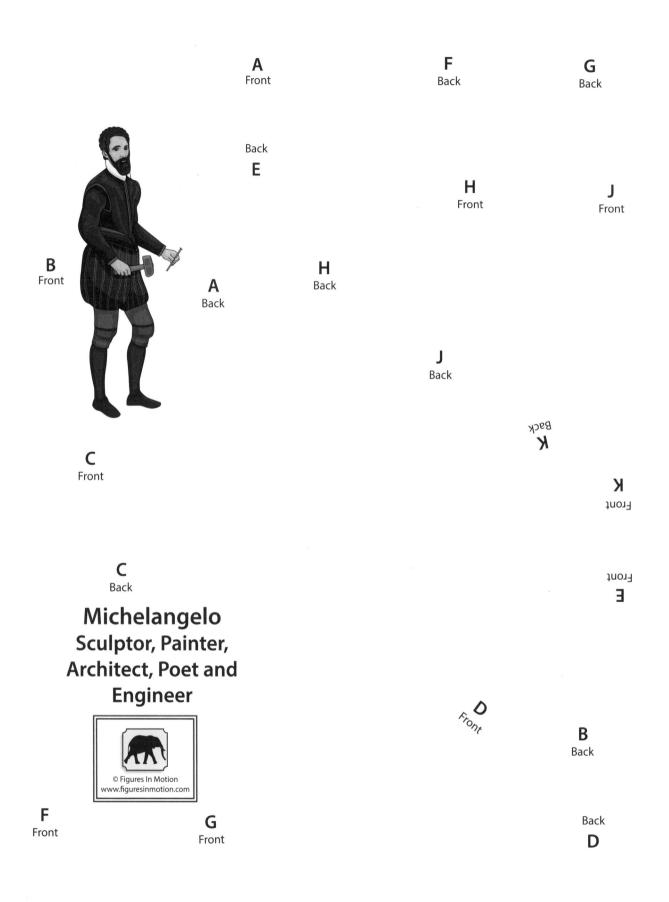

A
Front

F
Back

G
Back

Back
E

H
Front

J
Front

B
Front

A
Back

H
Back

J
Back

C
Front

K
Back

K
Front

C
Back

E
Front

Michelangelo
Sculptor, Painter, Architect, Poet and Engineer

© Figures In Motion
www.figuresinmotion.com

D
Front

B
Back

F
Front

G
Front

Back
D

G
Back

F
Back

A
Back

B
Back

Martin Luther
Monk, Theologian, and Key Figure of Protestant Reformation

E
Front

E
Back

C
Front

B
Front

C
Back

G
Front

F
Front

D
Back

A
Front

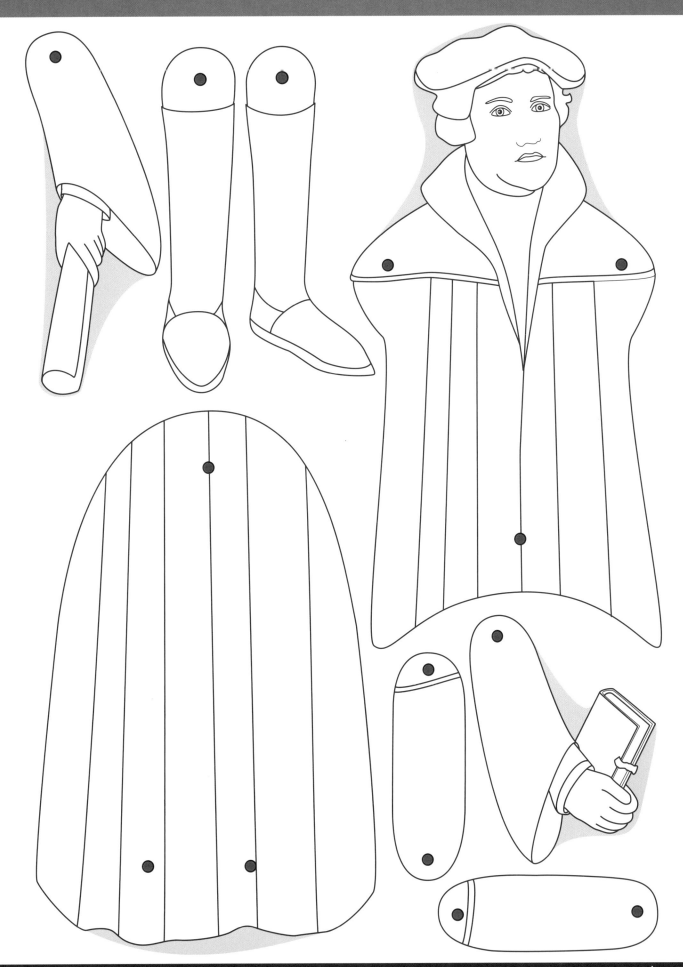

G
Back

F
Back

D
Front

A
Back

B
Back

Martin Luther
Monk, Theologian, and Key Figure of Protestant Reformation

E
Front

E
Back

C
Front

B
Front

C
Back

G
Front

F
Front

D
Back

A
Front

A

Back

Front

E

Front

F

Henry VIII
King of England

A

Front

B

Front

B

Back

F

Back

© Figures In Motion
www.figuresinmotion.com

D

Front

C

Front

Back

C

Back

D

E
Back

A
Back

E
Front

F
Front

Henry VIII
King of England

B
Front

F
Back

A
Front

B
Back

D
Front

C
Front

C
Back

D
Back

A
Front

B
Front

C
Front

Elizabeth I
Queen of England and Ireland

A
Back

B
Back

D
Back

© Figures In Motion
www.figuresinmotion.com

E
Front

D
Front

A
Front

B
Front

C
Front

Elizabeth I
Queen of England and Ireland

© Figures In Motion
www.figuresinmotion.com

A
Back

B
Back

D
Back

E
Front

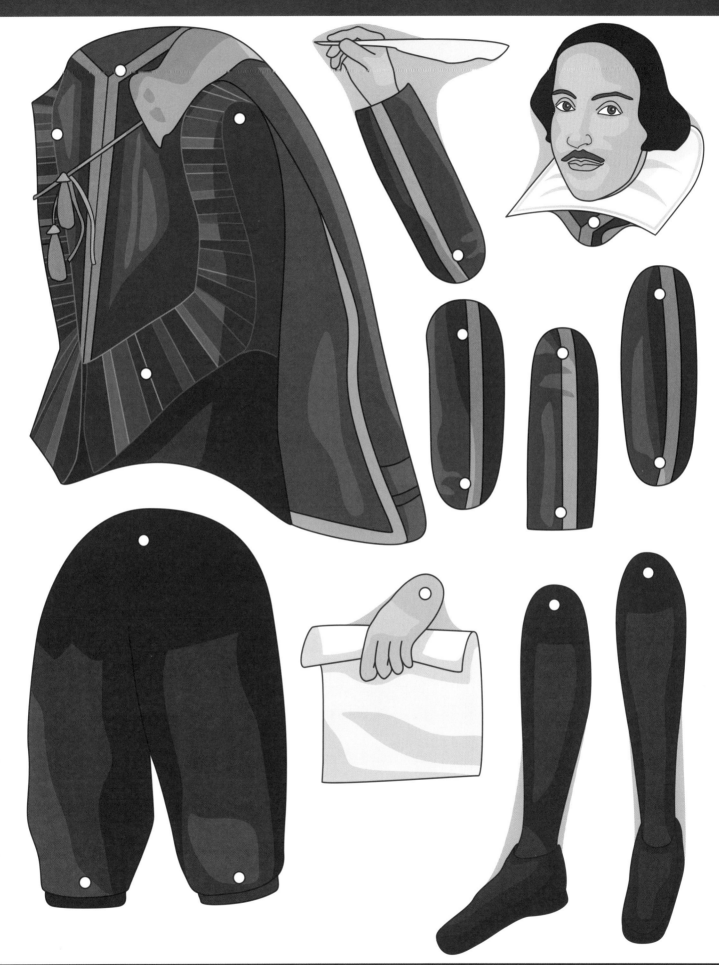

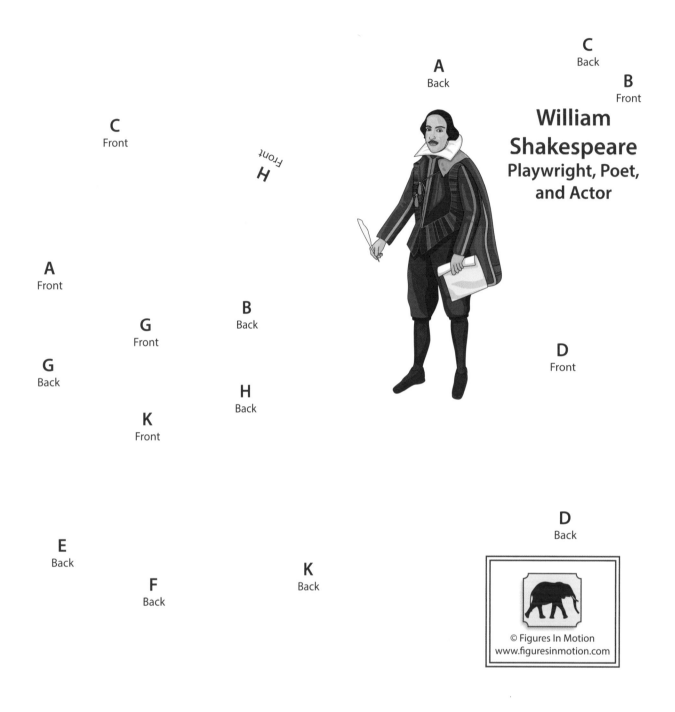

C
Back

A
Back

B
Front

William
Shakespeare
Playwright, Poet, and Actor

C
Front

H
Front

A
Front

G
Front

B
Back

D
Front

G
Back

H
Back

K
Front

D
Back

E
Back

F
Back

K
Back

E
Front

F
Front

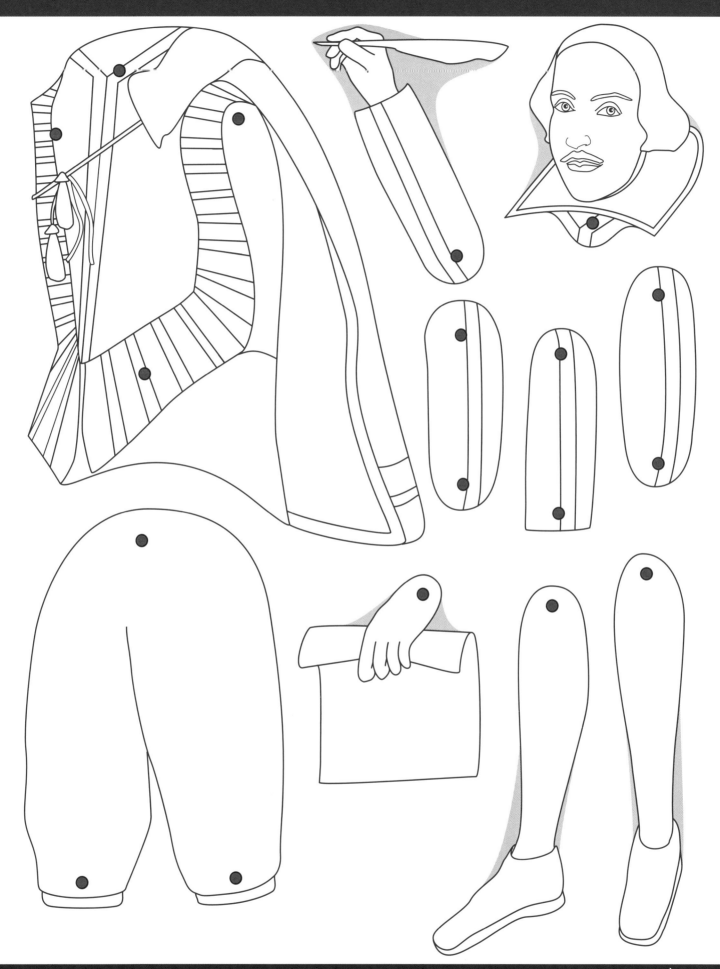

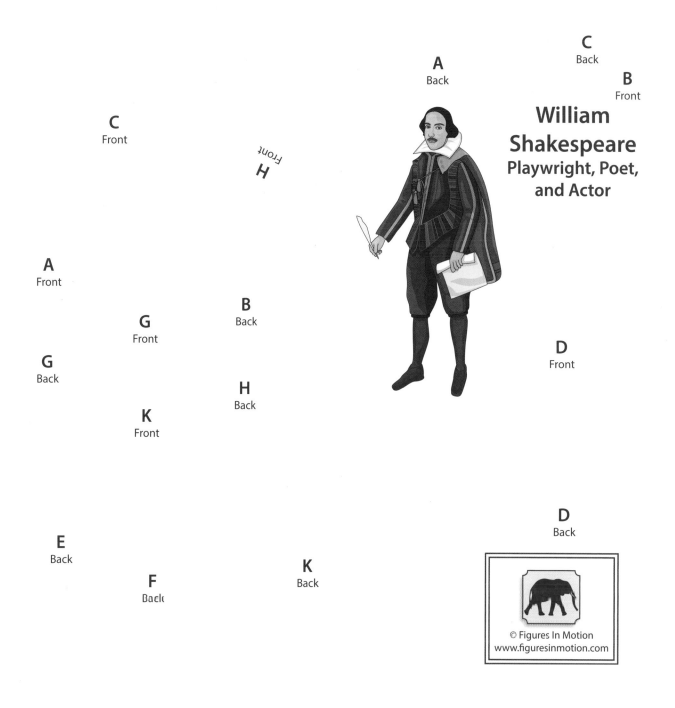

C
Back

A
Back

B
Front

William Shakespeare
Playwright, Poet, and Actor

C
Front

H
Front

A
Front

G
Front

B
Back

G
Back

H
Back

K
Front

D
Front

D
Back

E
Back

F
Back

K
Back

© Figures In Motion
www.figuresinmotion.com

E
Front

F
Front

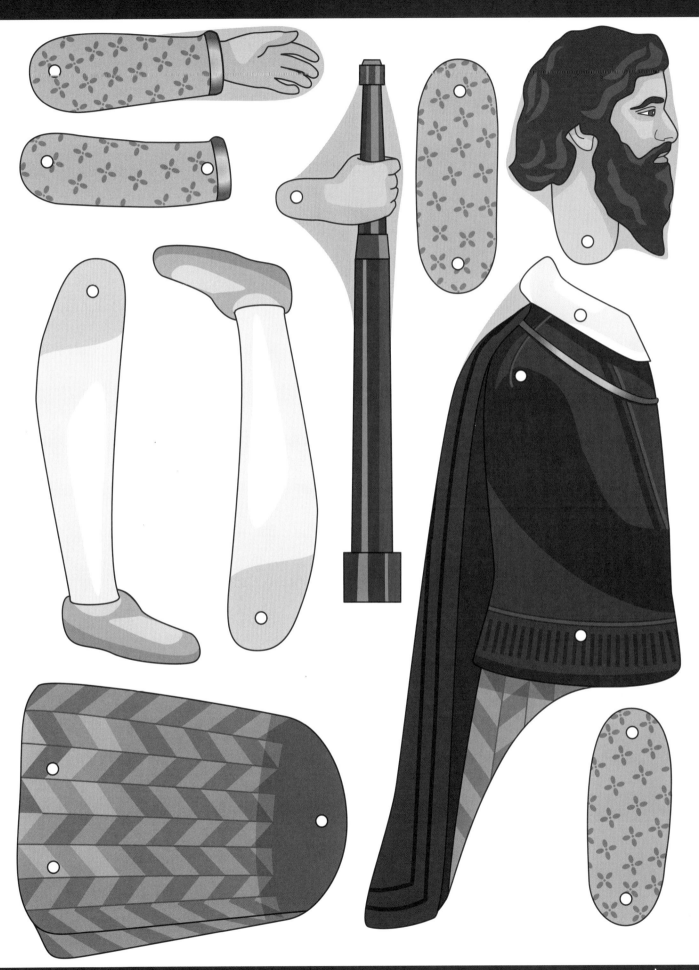

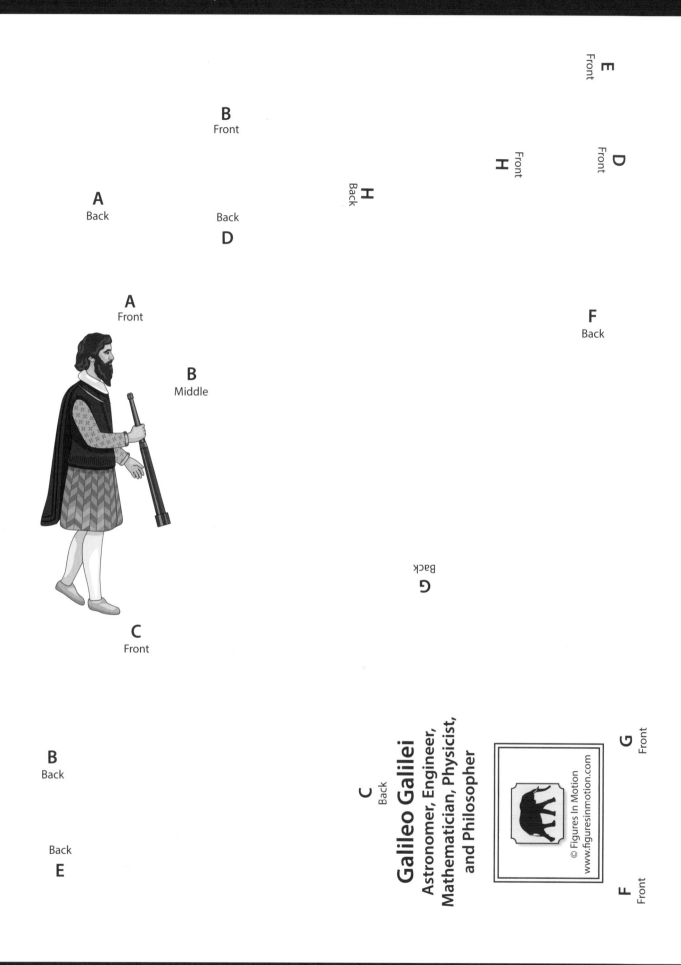

E
Front

B
Front

D
Front

H
Front

H
Back

A
Back

Back
D

A
Front

F
Back

B
Middle

C
Front

G
Back

B
Back

G
Front

Back
E

C
Back

F
Front

Galileo Galilei
Astronomer, Engineer,
Mathematician, Physicist,
and Philosopher

© Figures In Motion
www.figuresinmotion.com

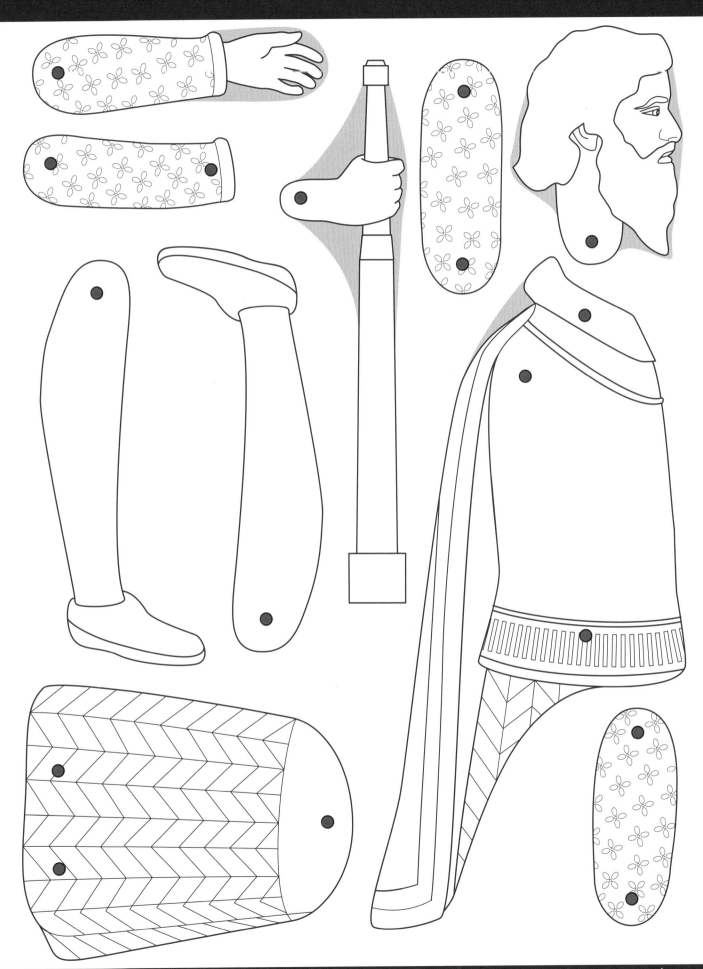

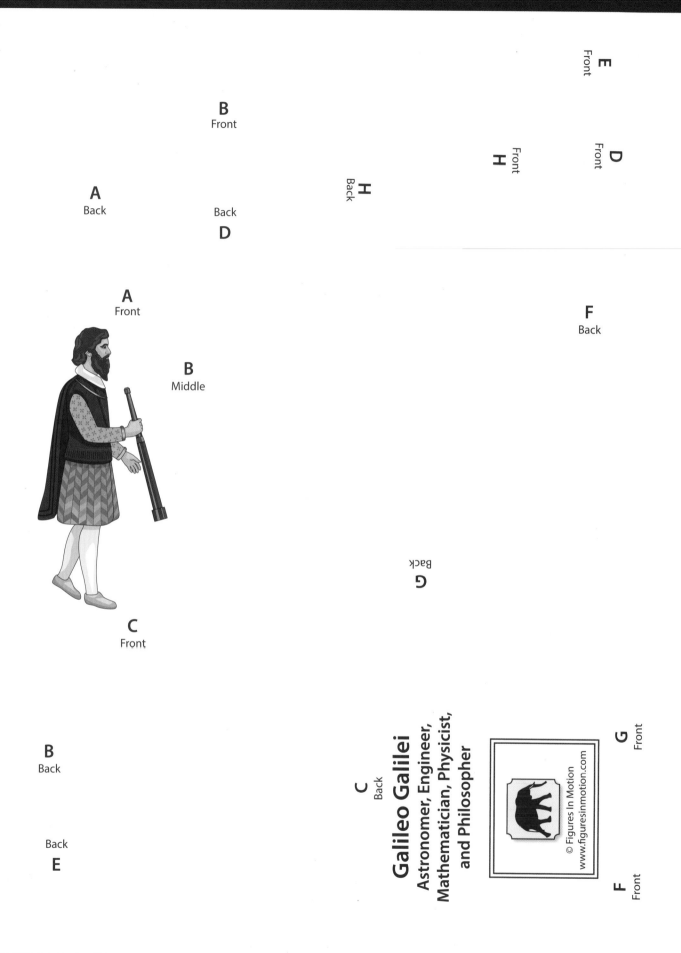

E
Front

B
Front

H
Front

D
Front

H
Back

A
Back

Back
D

A
Front

F
Back

B
Middle

G
Back

C
Front

B
Back

G
Front

C
Back

Galileo Galilei
Astronomer, Engineer,
Mathematician, Physicist,
and Philosopher

© Figures In Motion
www.figuresinmotion.com

F
Front

Back
E

MAKE A MOVING FIGURE

Making a moving figure from the Renaissance is easy. Before getting started, gather the following: coloring supplies (crayons, colored pencils, markers, or paint), scissors, ⅛″ hole punch, and mini brads (⅛″) or brass fasteners. Note: When using brass fasteners to assemble the figures, you may use a standard-size hole punch (with larger holes). Punch and fasteners are available from most craft stores or through the publisher at FiguresInMotion.com.

COLOR

- Use crayons, colored pencils, markers, or paint to color the figures.

CUT

- Remove the page of the figure to be assembled by tearing at the perforation along the book spine.
- Cut out each of the figure pieces. To make cutting easier, younger children can cut outside the shaded areas around intricate parts.
- Punch out the holes for the fasteners with a hole punch. The holes are colored red in the black-and-white figures to make hole identification easier.

ASSEMBLE

- Place the figure pieces face down (back side up) so that the assembly letters and figure name are visible.
- Match the letters together. A Front goes with A Back. B Front goes with B Back, etc.
- Place the pieces marked Front under the pieces marked Back as you look at the back side of the figure. Place the pieces marked Middle between the Front and Back pieces.
- Double check to make sure that all of the letters are matched together and that they are in the correct order. In some figures there may be more than two pieces that will be attached by one fastener.
- Insert the mini brad or fastener from the front side of the figure into the holes of the pieces to be joined together. The prongs of the brad or fastener should come out of the back side of the figure pieces.
- Separate the two prongs. Press them flat on the back side of the figure.
- Repeat until all of the holes are joined with brads or fasteners.
- The figure is assembled. Have fun playing!

ABOUT THE AUTHOR

Cathy Diez-Luckie brings the past alive by integrating art and history in her award-winning activity books for children. Movable action figures captivate and engage children as they learn about the great leaders of history.

Diez-Luckie's art has appeared nationally and internationally in numerous illustrated reference books, children's books, and magazines. Trained at the Toledo Museum of Art and the Academy of Art University in San Francisco, she also holds a graduate degree from Stanford University. She lives in Livermore, California, with her husband and three children, who happily test-drive her movable figure prototypes.

Discover the magic of history and the wonder of the past with children's activity books from Figures In Motion. These unique books make history come alive and allow children to explore their world and *learn by playing*. Make moving action figures of the most recognized men and women of history. Act out the real stories of history or make up your own and travel through time with moving figures! The series includes *Famous Figures of Ancient Times, Famous Figures of Medieval Times, Famous Figures of the Renaissance, Famous Figures of the American Revolution, Famous Figures of the Civil War,* and *Dinosaurs on the Move.*

Our *Footsteps of Faith* series brings Bible history alive with Queen Esther, David and Goliath, and others. Learn more about our books at FiguresInMotion.com.

Internet-linked scripts, coloring pages, puzzles, and activities are available at FiguresInMotion.com.

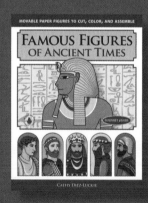
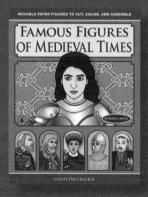
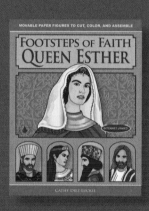

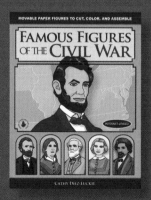
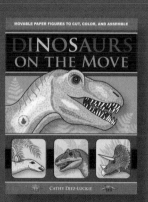